ENGLIS *Alive*

Approach Level

Barry Scholes and Gill Atha

Collins Educational

To the teacher

Outline of the course:

Level	Age	Pupil's Book	Listening Skills Cassettes	Computer Software (Adventures in English)
Starter	5+	Starter Masters Starter Books	Starter Cassette	——— ———
Approach	6-7	Approach Book	Approach Cassette	Goblin Winter
Level 1	7-8	Book 1	Level 1 Cassette	Spooky Towers
Level 2	8-9	Book 2	Level 2 Cassette	Spellbound
Level 3	9-10	Book 3	Level 3 Cassette	Pirate's Treasure
Level 4	10-11	Book 4	Level 4 Cassette	Wreckers' Rock
Level 5	11-12	Book 5	Level 5 Cassette	McGinty's Gold

English Alive! is a complete Primary English course in seven levels, covering the age range 5+ to 12+. It has been designed with full regard to the recommendations of the *Bullock Report* and the National Curriculum. It is carefully and systematically structured to develop the full range of English skills: speaking, listening, reading and writing and the study of language.

These skills are developed within the context of carefully chosen themes which link language development with other areas of the curriculum and offer wide scope for a variety of follow-up work. The literary extracts which provide the stimuli for many of these themes have been selected to extend the experience of the children.

The course begins in the Infant Department with photocopiable Starter sheets, and three Starter work books. An Approach Level then leads on to the main part of the programme in Levels 1-5.

At each level an audio cassette provides a structured approach to the development of listening skills. Each tape links with photocopiable masters in the Teacher's Resource Book.

Also available is the *Adventures in English* series of computer programs. Each adventure links with one of the books and is accompanied by Pressure-fax Spiritmaster activity sheets which provide a variety of stimulating follow-up work.

The **Approach Book** is the first full-format book in the *English Alive* course. Each double-paged unit features a separate theme, although units are grouped together to provide a wider focus on four aspects of the children's experience: the environment, time and the weather, animals and leisure. Unit 1 is similar in style to the earlier Starter Books, but later units gradually evolve into the style and layout of **Level 1**.

The units cover reading, writing and language skills. The accompanying *Teacher's Resource Book* features a variety of photocopiable masters which extend and complement these skills, and are designed to suit the ability range found in most classrooms. Ideas for the development of speaking skills are also included in the Teacher's Book. The Approach Level is completed by an audio cassette which provides for a carefully structured development of listening skills.

Contents

A Busy Street

Bakery

Newsagent

POST OFFICE

How many?

1 How many cars can you see?

2 How many buses can you see?

3 How many shops can you see?

4 How many children are there?

5 How many policemen are there?

Yes or no?

1 Is the bus red?

2 Can you see two vans?

3 Is a lady carrying a shopping bag?

4 Is there a post office in the picture?

5 Are there any traffic lights?

True or false?
Copy the sentences which are **true** about the picture.

1   A little girl is crying.
2   A man is going into the post office.
3   The bus has broken down.
4   The traffic lights are on green.
5   The policeman is looking in a shop window.
6   The bus is going to Smith St.

A busy street you know
1   What is the name of a busy street you know?
2   What kinds of shops are there on this street?
3   Which is your favourite shop?
4   What do you like to buy there?
5   How do you cross this busy street safely?

Shopping

Mr. Green

Mr. Chop

Mr. Bun

Shopkeepers

Copy and complete.

1 Mr. Bun makes bread. He is a _____.
2 Mr. Codd sells fish. He is a _____.
3 Mr. Chop sells meat. He is a _____.
4 Mr. Rice sells tea, sugar and flour. He is a _____.
5 Mr. Green sells fruit and vegetables. He is a _____.

Who?

1 Who sells cakes?
2 Who sells apples?
3 Who sells sausages?
4 Who sells fish?
5 Who sells tea?

Fishmonger

Mr. Codd

GROCER

Mr. Rice

Look at these shopping lists.

Mrs. Brown
tea
butter
coffee
soup

Mrs. Jones
pork chops
sausages
chicken
leg of lamb

Mr. Smith
bananas
potatoes
onions
cabbage

Copy and complete.
1   Mrs. Brown will buy from Mr. _____.
2   Mrs. Jones will go to Mr. _____.
3   Mr. Smith will buy from Mr. _____.

pears
baked beans
muffins
apples
oranges
lamb chops
cod
sausages
rice

Mrs. Bell's shopping list

1   What will Mrs. Bell buy from Mr. Green?
2   What will she buy from Mr. Chop?
3   What will she buy from Mr. Rice?
4   What will she buy from Mr. Bun?
5   What will she buy from Mr. Codd?

Going shopping
Write about a shopping trip with your mother or father.
What did you buy?
Which shop did you like best?

7

In the Playground

In the Playground

In the playground
Some run round
Chasing a ball
Or chasing each other;
Some pretend to be
Someone on TV;
Some walk
And talk,
Some stand
On their hands
Against the wall
And some do nothing at all.

Stanley Cook

About the poem

Here are some of the things the children do in the playground.

pretend	stand	run	do	talk	walk

Choose the right word.

1 Some children _____ around chasing a ball.
2 Some _____ to be someone on TV.
3 Other children _____ or _____.
4 Some _____ on their hands.
5 Other children _____ nothing at all.

Is and are

We say one girl **is** skipping, but two girls **are** skipping.

Look at the picture. Copy these sentences and put **is** or **are** in these spaces.

1 Some boys_____ playing football.
2 A girl_____ leaning against the wall.
3 Three girls_____ skipping.
4 The teacher_____ talking to some boys.
5 One boy_____ standing on his hands.
6 Some children_____ playing Hop-scotch.

Playtime

Look at the pictures and answer these questions.

1 Where are the children?   The children _____.
2 What is the teacher doing?   The teacher _____.
3 How many girls can you see?   I can see _____.
4 How many boys are chasing a ball?   There are _____.

Answer these questions with sentences of your own.

1 Who are your friends at school?
2 What is your favourite game?
3 What games do you play in winter?

My Day

I get up at eight o'clock

School starts at nine o'clock.

I eat my lunch at twelve o'clock.

I go home from school at four o'clock.

I have my tea at five o'clock.

I go to bed at eight o'clock.

Sue's day

Look at the pictures.

What time does Sue get up? Sue gets up at _____.

What happens at nine o'clock? At nine o'clock _____.

What time does she go home from
school? She goes home _____.

What happens at five o'clock? At five o'clock she ___.

What time does she go to bed? She _____.

These sentences are in the wrong order. Use the pictures to
help you write them out in the order they happened.

At twelve o'clock she ate up all her lunch.
She arrived at school just in time.
At eight o'clock she went to bed.
Sue got up and dressed for school.
She had her tea at five o'clock.
School finished at four o'clock.

Before and after

Copy these sentences putting in **before** or **after.**

Sue gets dressed _____ she gets up.

She goes home from school _____ she eats her tea.

The teacher marks her work _____ she has done it.

Sue washes her face _____ it gets dirty.

She cleans her teeth _____ she goes to bed.

She goes to sleep _____ she gets into bed.

My day

Write six sentences about your day.

I get up at _____. School ends _____.

Our school opens at _____. I have my tea _____.

I have my lunch _____. I go to bed _____.

Days of the Week

Monday's Child

Monday's child is fair of face,
Tuesday's child is full of grace,
Wednesday's child is full of woe,
Thursday's child has far to go,
Friday's child is loving and giving,
Saturday's child works hard for a living,
But the child that's born on the Sabbath day
Is bonny and blithe and good and gay.

Traditional

Read **Monday's Child,** and then look at the four pictures.
Copy and complete.

1 The girl who is crying was born on _____.
2 The man who is working hard was born on _____.
3 The girl who is walking was born on _____.
4 The boy hugging his mummy was born on _____.

Now answer these.
1 On which day were you born?
2 Do you think the poem is true about you?
3 Is it true about your friends?

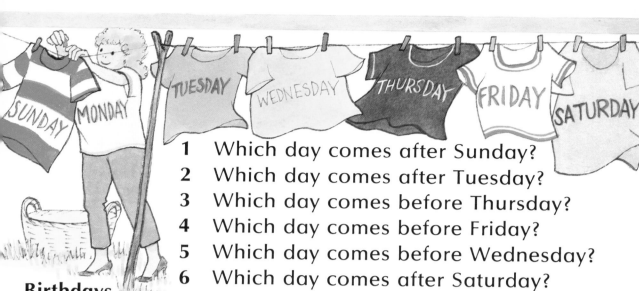

1 Which day comes after Sunday?
2 Which day comes after Tuesday?
3 Which day comes before Thursday?
4 Which day comes before Friday?
5 Which day comes before Wednesday?
6 Which day comes after Saturday?

Birthdays

Look at this graph of children's birthdays.

	6	5	4	3	2	1
Sun	Mon	Tue	Wed	Thur	Fri	Sat

1 How many children have birthdays on Monday?
2 How many children have birthdays on Friday?
3 How many were born on Saturday?
4 How many were born on Thursday?
5 Which day has the most birthdays?
6 Which days have the fewest birthdays?

Writing

Write the days of the week in your best writing. Remember to begin each one with a capital letter.
Which is your favourite day? Write about why you like it.

The Weather

Sunday

Weather words

icy

windy

sunny

rainy

cloudy

foggy

snowy

Monday

Tuesday

Wednesday

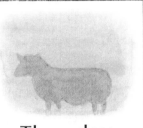

Thursday

Friday

Saturday

Copy and complete

1　It was snowing on _____.
2　It was foggy on _____.
3　On Sunday it was _____.
4　On Tuesday it was _____.
5　Wednesday was a _____ day.
6　Monday was a _____ day.
7　It was _____ on Friday.

True or false?

1　It was raining on Monday.
2　We could build a snowman on Saturday.
3　On Wednesday it was cloudy and dull.
4　Paul's hat blew off on Tuesday.
5　It was foggy on Friday.

14

Which colour?

Rainbow words

red	orange
yellow	green
blue	indigo
	violet

1 A banana is _____.
2 A fire-engine is _____.
3 Grass is _____.
4 The sky is _____.
5 A lemon is _____, but an orange is_____.

Opposites

wet   dry   hot   cold   sunny   dull

1 Yesterday it was dry, but today it is _____.
2 Ice is cold, but fire is _____.
3 I like sunny days better than _____ days.

A Windy Day

Write this story of a windy day.

Use the word bank to help you.

windy	hat	blow	off	chase	chasing
catch	catching	give	giving	thank	thanking

The Seasons

Owl at Home

Owl opened his door very wide.
'Come in, Winter,' said Owl.
'Come in and warm yourself for a while.'
Winter came into the house.
It came in very fast.
A cold wind pushed Owl against the wall.
Winter ran around the room.
It blew out the fire in the fire-place.
The snow whirled up the stairs
and whooshed down the hallway.
'Winter!' cried Owl.
'You are my guest.
This is no way to behave!'

From *Owl at Home* by Arnold Lobel

True or false?

Copy the sentences which are **true** about the story.

Owl opened his window wide.
Owl asked Winter to come into his house.
A cold wind pushed Owl against the wall.

Owl ran round the room.
Winter blew out the fire.
Winter sat down in Owl's chair.
Snow whirled up the stairs.
Owl told Winter to behave.

The Seasons

winter

autumn

spring

summer

1 Which season is warmest?
2 Which season is coldest?
3 Which season follows winter?
4 Which season follows spring?
5 Which season follows summer?
6 Which season follows autumn?
7 Which season are we in now?
8 Write down the seasons in order. Begin with spring.

Draw two pictures of yourself, one in summer clothes and the other in winter clothes. Write the names of 3 things you wear in summer, and 3 things you wear in winter.

The Snowman

Write this story about the snowman. Use the word bank to help you.

sun
melt
finish
children
snowman
build   shine
pleased   girl
sad   boy   hot

Animals' Houses

Animals' Houses

Of animals' houses
  Two sorts are found —
Those which are square ones
  And those which are round.

Square is a hen-house,
  A kennel, a sty:
Cows have square houses
And so have I.

A snail's shell is curly,
  A bird's nest round;
Rabbits have twisty burrows
  Underground.

But the fish in the bowl
  And the fish at sea —
Their houses are round
  As a house can be.

James Reeves

About the poem

1 What two shapes of animals' houses are there?

2 What shape is a hen-house?

3 Which animal lives underground?

4 What shape is the home of a fish?

5 Is your house round or square?

kennel   sty   shell   nest

Copy and complete.

1 A dog lives in a _____.

2 A bird lives in a _____.

3 A pig lives in a _____.

4 A snail lives in a _____.

In the garden

Look at this picture of the Brown family in the garden. Here are some sentences about the picture, but the beginnings and endings have been mixed up. Join each beginning to its proper ending.

The Brown family	lives in a bowl.
Rover the dog	lives in a hutch.
The rabbit	lives in a kennel.
A goldfish	lives in a big house.

Use these words to help you to answer these questions.

dog	cleaning	mummy	playing	daddy
rabbit	Carol	garden	John	hutch

1 Who can you see in the picture? I can see _____.
2 Where are they?   They are in _____.
3 What are John and his daddy doing?
   John and his daddy are _____.
4 What are Carol and her mummy doing?
   Carol and her mummy are _____.

Fox Tricks

Fox Tricks

'What a beautiful bird I am,' clucked Cock to himself. He smoothed his feathers and stuck out his chest. Then he crowed loudly to tell the world how grand he was.

Fox got up and trotted to the fence. 'Good morning, Cock,' he said. 'You are singing well today.'

'Thank you, Fox,' said Cock. 'I do have a fine voice, even if I say so myself.'

'Will you sing something just for me?' asked Fox.

'I would be glad to,' said Cock. He closed his eyes, threw back his head, and crowed loudly again.

Fox saw his chance. He sprang up, grabbed Cock by the throat, and ran off.

From *Fox Tricks* by Aidan Chambers

Yes or no?

1   Does the cock think he is ugly?
2   Were the cock's eyes shut when he sang?
3   Did the fox say he liked the cock's singing?
4   Does the cock think he has a good voice?
5   Is the cock caught by the fox?

Word building

Dan is making some new words in his wall. He is adding **er** to some words you already know. Write down and read the other new words Dan will make.

Farmer   sing _____   light _____   tall _____   play _____

Now use the words in these sentences:

A_____ works on a farm.

Feathers are _____ than stones.

I like singing. I am a good_____.

John is_____ than Jim.

I listen to records on my record_____.

Odd-man-out

Which of these animals is the odd-man-out?

1 chicken   hen   fox
2 fox   rabbit   wolf
3 fish   gorilla   monkey
4 turtle   crab   elephant
5 peacock   rat   mouse

Read the story **Fox Tricks** again. Do you think this is the end of the story? Will the fox gobble up the cock or do you think the cock will escape?

Tell the story in your own words and add your own ending.

A Bed for a Penguin

Grandma's Own Zoo

'Right,' said Grandma. Without any fuss, she picked up the penguin and carried it into the bathroom. Plonk! Into the water. Tim had a gorgeous time scooping cupfuls of water over the bird and dripping a face flannel over its head.

The penguin seemed to be enjoying himself. He lay on his back and kicked his legs. Then he got up, and tried to climb up the side of the bath, obviously for the pleasure of sliding down again. He was quite a bird!

'What's his name?' asked Tim.

'I don't recognise this one,' Grandma had to admit, 'but he's making me feel dizzy.'

'Then we'll call him "Dizzy",' said Tim. 'Where's he going to sleep?'

'In the bath,' said Grandma.

And there they left him for the night.

From *Grandma's Own Zoo* by Phyllis Arkle

Joanne has written about this story but her sentences are muddled. Put them into the right order so that they tell the story properly.

Tim poured water on the penguin.
The penguin was taken to the bathroom.
Tim called the penguin "Dizzy."
Grandma put the penguin in the bath.
The penguin liked sliding.

Alphabetical order

a b c d e f g h i j k l m n o p q r s t u v w x y z

Can you say the alphabet without looking?

Put these animals into alphabetical order.
Remember that cat comes before dog because the **c** of cat comes before the **d** of dog in the alphabet.

1	dog	monkey	cat
2	zebra	giraffe	elephant
3	duck	mouse	puppy
4	cow	bird	horse
5	sheep	donkey	pig

Writing
Pretend that you have a very unusual pet.
It may be a monkey, a giraffe or even a hippopotamus.

Write a story about it.

Charlie's Piano

Stick to it, Charlie

When they had gone, Mum fetched a duster and gave the piano a polish.

Charlie opened the lid covering the keys.

'Some of the ivories are missing,' he observed.

'They need a clean.' Mum stopped polishing, licked her finger and rubbed one of them. 'They're very dirty and rather yellow.'

'Like Mrs Sharp's teeth.'

'Charlie! What a thing to say! Anyway, she seemed very nice when we went round last night to fix a time for your lesson.'

Charlie pressed down some keys.

'Cor!' He screwed up his face. 'It's terribly jangly.'

'It wants tuning, I expect.' Dad came into the room. 'Let's open the top.'

Charlie stood on the stool and peered inside.

'POOH! It's very smelly, too.'

'I'm not surprised,' laughed Dad. 'There's a mouldy bun, an old piece of cheese and a half-eaten apple inside.'

From *Stick to it, Charlie* by Joy Allen

Answer in sentences.

1 Who polished the piano?
2 What colour were the dirty ivories?
3 What is Charlie's piano teacher called?
4 Who else came into the room?
5 What was inside the piano?

One and more than one

Here is one drum.

But here are two drum**s**.

I can see one bus.

He can see two bus**es**.

Copy and complete.

Here are two _____.

Tim has three _____.

My cat has two _____.

Mary is holding two _____.

Mum has just picked some _____.

Word building

talk play build ing cook fish ing ing ing ng

Dan is building again. This time he is making new words by adding **ing.**

Finish these for him.

| build _____ | play _____ | talk _____ | cook _____ | fish _____ |

Now copy these sentences putting in one of the new words you have made.

Dan is _____ a wall.

John and Ranjit were _____ in the river.

I was _____ to my friend today.

Dad was _____ chips for tea.

Tim was _____ his piano.

flute

found golden

music

treasure

wish

magic

The Magic Flute

This is a magic flute. It will grant you three wishes.

Write a story about it.

Here are some words to help you.

The Present

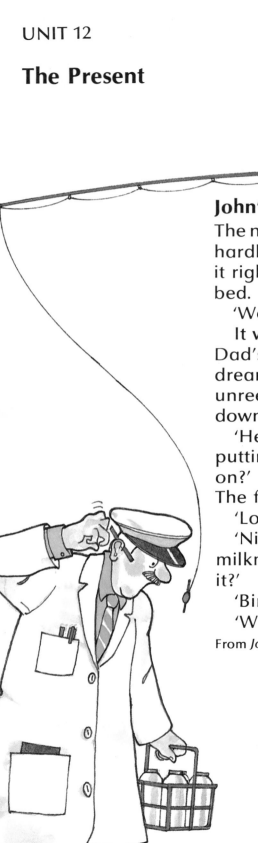

John's First Fish

The next day, John got his fishing rod. He could hardly believe his eyes. He woke up and found it right under his nose, propped against the bed.

'Wow!' he yelled. 'What a beauty!'

It was a real one, a **man's** one, just like Dad's. It was ten times better than he had ever dreamed of. He ran to the window and unreeled it, watching the float go dangling down to the street.

'Here!' shouted the milkman, who was just putting the bottles on the step. 'What's going on?'

The float dangled in front of his nose.

'Look out!' yelled John. 'I'll have your hat!'

'Nice rod you've got there,' said the milkman. 'I like a bit of fishing myself. New is it?'

'Birthday,' said John.

'Wish it was mine,' said the milkman.

From *John's First Fish* by Helen Cresswell

Answer these questions.

1 What was John's present?
2 Where did he find it?
3 What did he do with it?
4 Who was outside John's house?
5 Was it a Christmas present?

Use the words to help you finish these sentences.

1 John's fishing rod was big. His dad's was———.
2 A mouse is small, but an ant is———.
3 A horse is———, but a car is faster.
4 A tortoise is slow, but a snail is———.
5 A tree is——— but a giant is taller.

What do you think these parcels are?

Writing

Imagine this parcel has just arrived
for you. Write a story about it.
Make your story as interesting as possible.
Here are some words to help you.

present	postman	parcel
deliver	open	surprise

label

An Invitation

Ambleside Cottage,
Newquay,
Cornwall.
29 July, 1988.

Dear Paul and Frances,
The _____ holidays are here again and we were both wondering if you would _____ to come and stay with us for two _____. We talked to your Mum and _____ and they said you could. There'll be lots to do, swimming in the _____ and building sandcastles on the _____.
We do hope you both want to _____.
See you soon.
Grandma + Grandad xxx

Copy the letter and fill in the missing words.
The word bank will help you.

beach   Dad   come
weeks   summer   like   sea

Holiday words

Here are some holiday words. Look for them in your dictionary and write down what they mean.

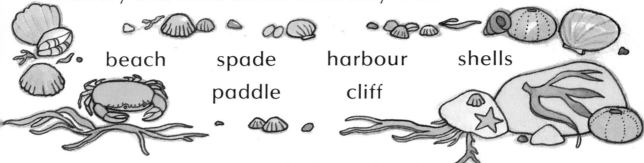

beach   spade   harbour   shells

paddle   cliff

Now put the words in alphabetical order.

Spot the sandcastles

Look carefully at these sandcastles.
Only **two** are exactly the same. Can you find them?

Writing

Pretend you are Paul or Frances.
Write a letter to Grandma and
Grandad saying that you would
like to spend the holidays with them.
Tell them all the things you'd like to do
when you are there.

Waves

There are Big Waves

There are big waves and little waves,
Green waves and blue,
Waves you can jump over,
Waves you dive through.

Waves that rise up
Like a great water wall,
Waves that swell softly
And don't break at all.

Waves that can whisper,
Waves that can roar,
And tiny waves that run at you
Running on the shore.

Eleanor Farjeon

Read the poem carefully. Answer these questions.

1 What colour are the waves?
2 What sounds do the waves make?
3 What do the tiny waves do?
4 What do the waves that rise up look like?

What am I?

I am blue.
I am wet.
Children paddle in me.
I am the_____.

I am green.
I live in the sea.
I am a plant.
I am_____.

I am hard.
Something used to live in me.
You find me on the beach.
I am a_____.

I am yellow.
You find me near the sea.
Children make castles
with me.
I am_____.

  sea   **Copy these sentences putting in the right word.**

1. The _____ is blue.
2. I can _____ the boats.
3. Look in the mirror. What can you _____?
4. We went for a paddle in the _____.
5. Far out at _____ I can _____ a ship.

Writing

Look at the postcard at the top of the page. Pretend you are on holiday and are going to send this card to someone. Write what you would put on the card. Do not forget the name and address.

On holiday

What is happening in this picture?
Imagine you are at the camp-site. How would you enjoy yourself?
Where would you sleep?
How is this holiday different from your last holiday?